EXTREME WORLD

THE WORLD'S MOST AMAZING ANIMALS

by Cari Meister

raintree

Capstone company — publishers for children

Raintree is an imprint of Capstone Global Library Limited, a company incorporated in England and Wales having its registered office at 264 Banbury Road, Oxford, OX2 7DY – Registered company number: 6695582

www.raintree.co.uk
myorders@raintree.co.uk

ISBN 978 1 3982 4761 1 (hardback)
ISBN 978 1 3982 4762 8 (paperback)

Editorial Credits
Editor: Christopher Harbo; Designer: Kay Fraser; Media Researcher: Svetlana Zhurkin; Production Specialist: Katy LaVigne

Image Credits
Getty Images: 500px/Robert Smits, 7, Adria Photography, 18, Gallo Images, 9, Stefano Cavanna, 8; Shutterstock: Albie Venter, 15, Chase Dekker, 6, Danita Delimont, 14. Dirk Ercken, 12, Graphics Illuminate, cover, 1, Johan Swanepoel, 16, Kurit Afshen, 13, Martin Mecnarowski, 19, Neil Bromhall, 5, Rob Jansen, 4, Sirisak_baokaew, 17, unoL, 11; Svetlana Zhurkin: 20, 21

All internet sites appearing in back matter were available and accurate when this book was sent to press.

British Library Cataloguing in Publication Data
A full catalogue record for this book is available from the British Library.

Printed and bound in India.

CONTENTS

Words in **bold** are in the glossary.

AMAZING ANIMALS

Some animals run very fast. Others crawl slowly. Some huge animals swim in the sea. Some tiny ones live in the ground under your feet. Other animals are really hairy. And some have no hair at all! The world is full of amazing animals!

Slow-moving sloth

Hairless naked mole rat

LARGE AND LOUD

The world's largest animal needs a lot of space! The blue whale can grow to be 30.5 metres (100 feet) long. That is nearly as long as three buses end to end!

The blue whale is also the loudest animal. It makes sounds as loud as a jet engine! These sounds can be heard by other whales many kilometres away.

MIGHTY STRONG

An African elephant can lift 318 kilograms (700 pounds) with its trunk. For its size, an eagle is even stronger. It can lift four times its body weight.

The horned dung beetle is the strongest animal for its size. This tiny insect is no bigger than a pea. But it can push poo balls that weigh 1,000 times more than it does!

DEADLY JELLIES

The see-through box jellyfish does not look dangerous. It floats in the water like a balloon. But watch out! It is deadly.

Box jellyfish have long **tentacles**. Each one can sting with powerful **venom**. More people die from box jellyfish stings than from shark attacks each year.

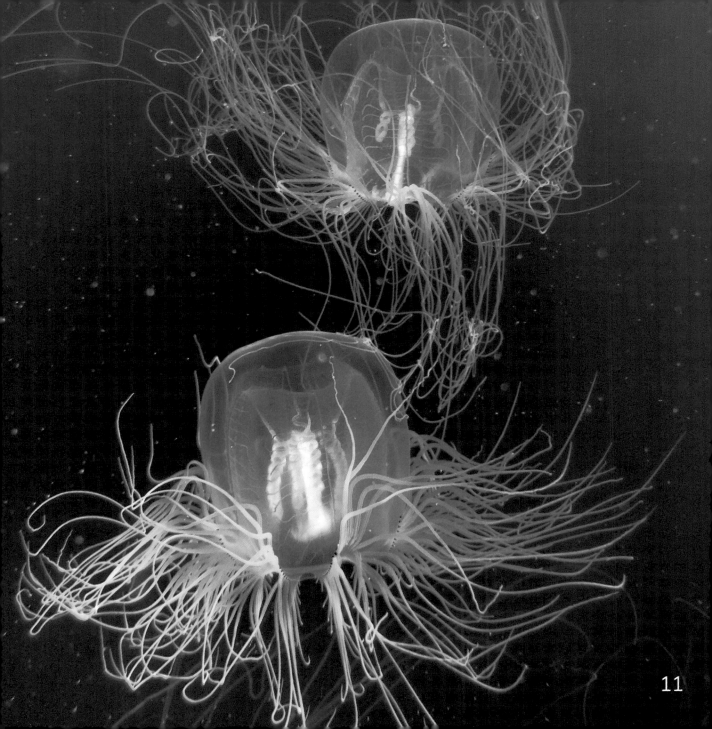

11

COLOURFUL CREATURES

Colourful animals make our world a beautiful place. Flashy parrots fly through the sky. Brightly-coloured **poison** dart frogs hop through the **rainforest**.

Poison dart frog

Panther chameleon

What is one of the most colourful animals? It is the chameleon! This lizard can change colours. It changes its colour to show its **mood**, to stay cool or to hide.

SPEEDY SPRINTERS

Some animals are built for speed.
The cheetah is the fastest land animal.
It uses its long legs to chase **prey**. It can
run as fast as a car on the motorway!

Cheetahs need to run fast to catch their food. They hunt a kind of antelope called an impala. Impalas are speedy too! They can run almost as fast as a cheetah.

HELPFUL HORNS

Horns are helpful! Some animals use them to scratch themselves. Others use their horns for **defence** or to fight.

Gemsbok fighting

The Asian water buffalo has the longest horns. From tip to tip, they can be longer than a bed! Water buffalo use their long horns to fight off tigers.

HAIR TO SPARE

Sea otters swim in ice-cold waters. How do they stay warm? They have the thickest fur of any animal. A sea otter can have up to 800 million hairs on its body!

From the sea to the desert, amazing animals are everywhere! They all have special **features** to help them **survive**. Which animal do you like best?

Scarlet macaws

LONG-HORN HEADBAND

The Asian water buffalo has the longest horns on Earth!
Make your own Asian water buffalo headband to see
what it is like to have such long horns.

WHAT YOU NEED

- scissors

- card

- masking tape

- 4 kitchen roll tubes

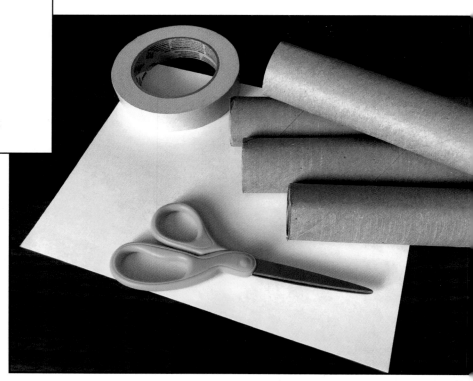

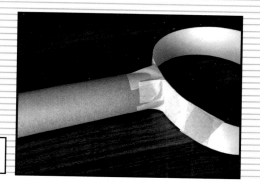

1. Cut two long strips of card that are about the width of three fingers.

2. Tape the two pieces of card end to end to make one long band.

3. Wrap the band snugly around your head and tape it to form a circular headband. Remove the headband and put it aside.

4. Tape two kitchen roll tubes together end to end to make a horn.

5. Repeat step 4 to make a second horn.

6. Tape both horns to the sides of the headband.

7. Put on your long-horn headband and imagine what it is like to be an Asian water buffalo!

GLOSSARY

defence an ability to protect oneself from harm

feature an important part or quality of something

mood the way that you are feeling

poison a substance that can kill or harm someone

prey an animal hunted by another animal for food

rainforest a thick forest where rain falls almost every day

survive to stay alive

tentacle a long, armlike body part some animals use to touch, grab or smell

venom a poisonous liquid produced by some animals

FIND OUT MORE

BOOKS

Cheetahs (Animals), Jaclyn Jaycox (Raintree, 2021)

Incredibly Colourful Creatures (Unreal but Real Animals), Megan Cooley Peterson (Raintree, 2023)

The Fascinating Animal Book for Kids: 500 Wild Facts!, Ginjer Clarke (Rockridge Press, 2020)

WEBSITES

DK Findout!: Blue Whale
dkfindout.com/us/animals-and-nature/whales-dolphins-and-porpoises/blue-whale

National Geographic Kids: Amazing Animals
kids.nationalgeographic.com/videos/topic/amazing-animals

ABOUT THE AUTHOR

Cari Meister has written more than 130 books for children, including the Tiny series (Penguin) and the Fast Forward Fairy Tales series (Scholastic). Cari is a school librarian who loves to visit other schools to talk about the joy of reading and writing. Cari lives in the mountains of Colorado, USA, with her husband, four boys, one horse and one dog. You can find out more about her at www.carimeister.com.

INDEX